THE TOWER OF BABEL

Also by William Wiesner

Joco and the Fishbone

the TOWER OF BABEL

william wiesner

THE VIKING PRESS   NEW YORK

Pic Bk 1. Bible—Stories

To the children of all nations

Many many years after the Great Flood, the descendants of Noah lived in the hill country at the foot of Mount Ararat. Although they were large in numbers, all the people spoke one language.

The time came when the people could not produce enough food on the mountainous land for themselves and their flocks, and they journeyed eastward.

They came upon a fertile plain and stopped at the banks of the river Euphrates. And they dwelt there.

Then they said one to another, "Come, let us bake bricks; we will build ourselves a city and become one nation, lest we be scattered over the earth."

At once they started to build the city on the banks of the river, and for protection they built a high wall around the town, with towers and strong gates.

They called the city Babel.

And they chose a king whose name was Nimrod.

He was a mighty king. All the fertile land far and wide was under his sway. He founded many cities, but Babel was the largest and the richest of them all.

Instead of being thankful and happy to live in that rich city in ease and luxury, Nimrod and his people became proud and insolent.

Nimrod rallied his people and said to them, "I, King of Babel and master over the land, shall build a tower, the like of which does not exist on earth, and it will be a testimony to our great power."

He ordered his architects to draw plans for a tower whose base was to be larger than the city itself.

The people were as presumptuous and insolent as their king. They complied with his request, and a multitude of workmen started to build the tower.

When the tower was almost five thousand feet high, the king inspected it and said to his architect, "Make it higher!"

And they put layer upon layer until the tower was ten thousand feet high.

But when King Nimrod looked up, he said, "Make it still higher!"

The workmen did as they were told. Still King Nimrod in his overreaching pride was not satisfied, and he shouted, "Build it higher—so high that it will reach into heaven, for from the top of this tower I will storm the heavens and be mightier than God."

The tower grew higher and higher until its top disappeared in the clouds.

God watched the mad ambition of King Nimrod and his people. He knew that as one people who spoke only one language they could not be kept from anything they wanted to do. And He said, "I shall confuse their language, that they may not understand one another's speech!"

In a moment God's will was done.

The greatest confusion broke out on the tower, because the workmen couldn't understand each other any more.

The bricklayer who had asked for clay was handed a pail of water.

The brick carrier brought great rough stones instead of bricks.

The growing misunderstandings led to ugly quarrels and fighting.

More and more the work slowed down. Finally the workmen laid down their tools and went home. Soon the entire tower was deserted.

The confusion spread all over the city. Pupils couldn't understand the language of their teacher, nor could the teacher understand his pupils. Neither could the children understand each other. So everybody went home.

Each family spoke only its own language. The markets closed since nobody could make himself understood. Tradesmen locked their stores. Craftsmen left their shops and the street vendors stopped crying their wares. Soon the confusion of languages was so great that all life in the city came to a standstill.

The people were filled with consternation. All of them, old and young, gathered in the square before the king's palace. They talked and talked, but since they couldn't understand each other, they began to shout, thinking that perhaps in that way they could make themselves understood.

When the din became unbearable, an officer of the guard stepped in front of the palace gate and tried to calm the people. But no one understood a single word.

The people began to push and quarrel and fight one another. The officer feared that the excited crowd might storm the palace. "Clear the square and disperse the people!" he ordered the royal guard.

But the guard, too, misunderstood the order. They did an about-face and chased King Nimrod with all his councilors through the gate and out of the town.

The people began to divide into small groups that spoke the same language. They moved away from each other, and found new places to live. They tilled new land and founded new cities. Thus the population was dispersed over the face of the whole earth.

In this way God confused the languages of mankind and divided one people into many nations.

The tower was never finished. It crumbled and fell into pieces. And there on the banks of the river Euphrates you can still see a heap of stone and rubble as high as a mountain that was once the Tower of Babel.

The story of the Tower of Babel as told here is based on the Book of Genesis and on commentaries to this Bible story in the book Hebrew Myths *by Robert Graves and Raphael Patai.*

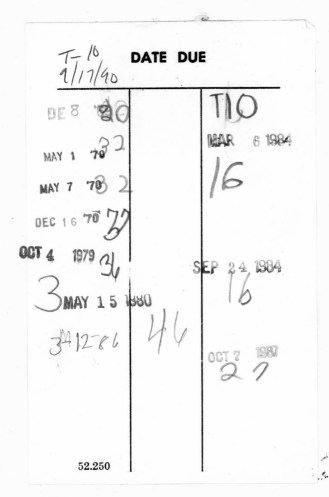